The story so far...

Mysti Rainbowfrost is a fairy who has been assigned to look after human teenager Ella Devonshire. But there's a problem. She doesn't want a fairy hanging around cramping her style, even though that fairy can bring certain advantages, like making her chumbas appear to be 32DD or joining her on a double date and saving her from a run-in with some local thugs. Ella would rather do things her own way, but she's slowly coming around to the idea that Mysti might just be useful. Sometimes. After all, Mysti has special powers and can transform into a human when she needs to.

Ella's younger sister, Abby, is more in tune with the idea of having a fairy for a friend. She helps her mother run a fairy shop on the Heath and is fascinated by the fairy world. She thinks Mysti is great.

But as Mysti becomes more involved in the human world she finds herself getting in trouble back home, because fairies must never try to be human. And they must always follow the rules.

Mysti

Ella xx

Abby x

Thorn Oakwood

Gorgeous fit fairy hunk and Mysti's heart throb.

Oh forget it, Pease. He's in love with Stardust... the most perfect fairy in Golden Heath. He's just being kind.

I heard what happened, Mysti...

Wow, Thorn spoke to you!

Oh, it was nothing Thorn*...

Thorn

10

That's not what I heard... saving three humans single handed... that's pretty impressive.

Mark this fairy hunk out of 10.

7

Meanwhile back at home...

Come on, Abby, get your skates on... Ella left for school ages ago.

I'm coming.

Is something worrying you?

It's not like you Abby... You used to hate being late for school.

Yeah... that's when school was fun... like ten years ago. When you had to choose between the DRESSING UP BOX and the DOUGH table. They don't even have a DOUGH table at my school.

No... it's OK... Like you said... I'll be late

 Dough

Coloured gunk that tastes terrible. Girls use it to make pretty flowers and animals and stuff. Boys throw it at each other and make a mess.

 Dressing up box

All those high heels, feather boas and party frocks. Girls go for the uniforms: fireman, policeman, even postman. The female need to control is apparent before the age of three.

11

Later in Ella's chemistry class...

Rachael Bunting arrives late...   The evil twins knock her over...

>BUMP!<

13

Why do they make us do this?

Concentrate, Abby... you missed a pass...

These uniforms were designed by the Marquis de Sade...

Really? I'm sure my mum got mine in Debenhams...

Sorry... OUCH!

WAKE UP, DEVONSHIRE!!...

I just wish I could see the point of all this...

Back in chemistry class, time has warped...

and the lesson is going on forever. Whoever controls these things in the universe has taken a nap and there is now nothing to stop this lesson lasting until the end of time. So you might as well learn something:

Chemistry

What you need to know:
1. Hydrogen sulphide stinks.
2. Iron filings make the lesson feel like Bonfire Night.
3. Phosphorus burns white.
4. Crocodile clips relieve the boredom in many imaginative ways.

Hey, Ella... I've got an idea...

Sir?

Hmm, ...yes...

Do you do home tutoring?

Um, er, ah, er that is, ah...

Never mind.

17

KA-BOOM!

You'll be relieved to hear that the loud explosion has woken up the napping controller in the universe we are now on fast forward... ...Yes, and the Ogre got her text and comes calling.

"Fe fi fo fum guess who smells the blood of a chemistry man?"

Everything alright Brian?

BRRRIINNNNGGGG

100% FAT

Class dismissed.

After the lesson, in Ella's office...

Why is everyone laughing at that girl?

Rachael..? Oh everyone laughs at Rachael... She doesn't mind. Anyway, she's a loser.

What has she lost?

Mysti... another time OK. I need my mobile back... and I have a plan... You fly into Ogre's office, transform into a human, grab my mobile, throw it out the window, transform back and fly out. OK?

So?

Losing the mobile was a punishment right?

If you're my friend you'll help me...

Well I'm not meant to use my powers to get you out of...

But I'll get in trouble and...

OK. Suit yourself.

Why is Ella asking me to do something that will get me in trouble?

21

Outside in first break...

Great. All I need. A useless fairy.
Well, I won't help you if you're going to be mean...
So, you'll help?
If you'll do something for me...
Yeah... of course... First let's get my mobile...

Mum said to remind you about your PIANO LESSON...
Shut up, splat... Got things to do.

I thought having a BROTHER was bad... he's a dream compared to her... At least he just beats me up... he doesn't verbally assassinate me every time I open my mouth.
Have you swallowed a dictionary or something? Anyway... she doesn't mean it. She can be OK sometimes.

i Piano lessons

If you are taking lessons and have no idea why, it is almost certainly because your parents didn't have the opportunity and you are being sacrificed for their dream. It is a well known fact that a large number of piano teachers are ugly sadistic harridans who hate children. Play safe. Take up the trombone.

i Brothers

Advantages:
Smaller ones can be cute and adoring.
Larger ones may have cute friends.
Disadvantages:
They beat you up.
They don't change their socks.

After school... the bullies lie in wait for Rachael...

29

After school in the fairy shop...

Abby and Imogen are helping out when...

Rachael bursts in...

Hello, dear. Can I help you?

Err... I'd like a...

Suddenly, at the worst moment...

Err... One of these...

I'm sorry... I don't seem to have your size... I'll just check my stock...

Perhaps Ella has no idea what it feels like to be bullied.

That's the problem... she's so popular and has so many friends... and she doesn't need me...

You know about that?

That's not true. You helped get her mobile back so she could contact Ollie...

Yes... and I won't tell Professor Dust. You're doing fine. Just be patient with Ella. And there's no reason you can't watch over this other girl... while you're looking after Ella of course.

School gates next morning...

You got it, fat girl?

Here... I couldn't get any more... My mum will know they're missing.

ALCO

Not our problem... So what have we got... three packets of fags... one bottle of voddie... and you don't tell a soul, right? Or we'll deny it. You'll get the blame for this if anyone finds out... got it?

33

Saturday morning at the shops...

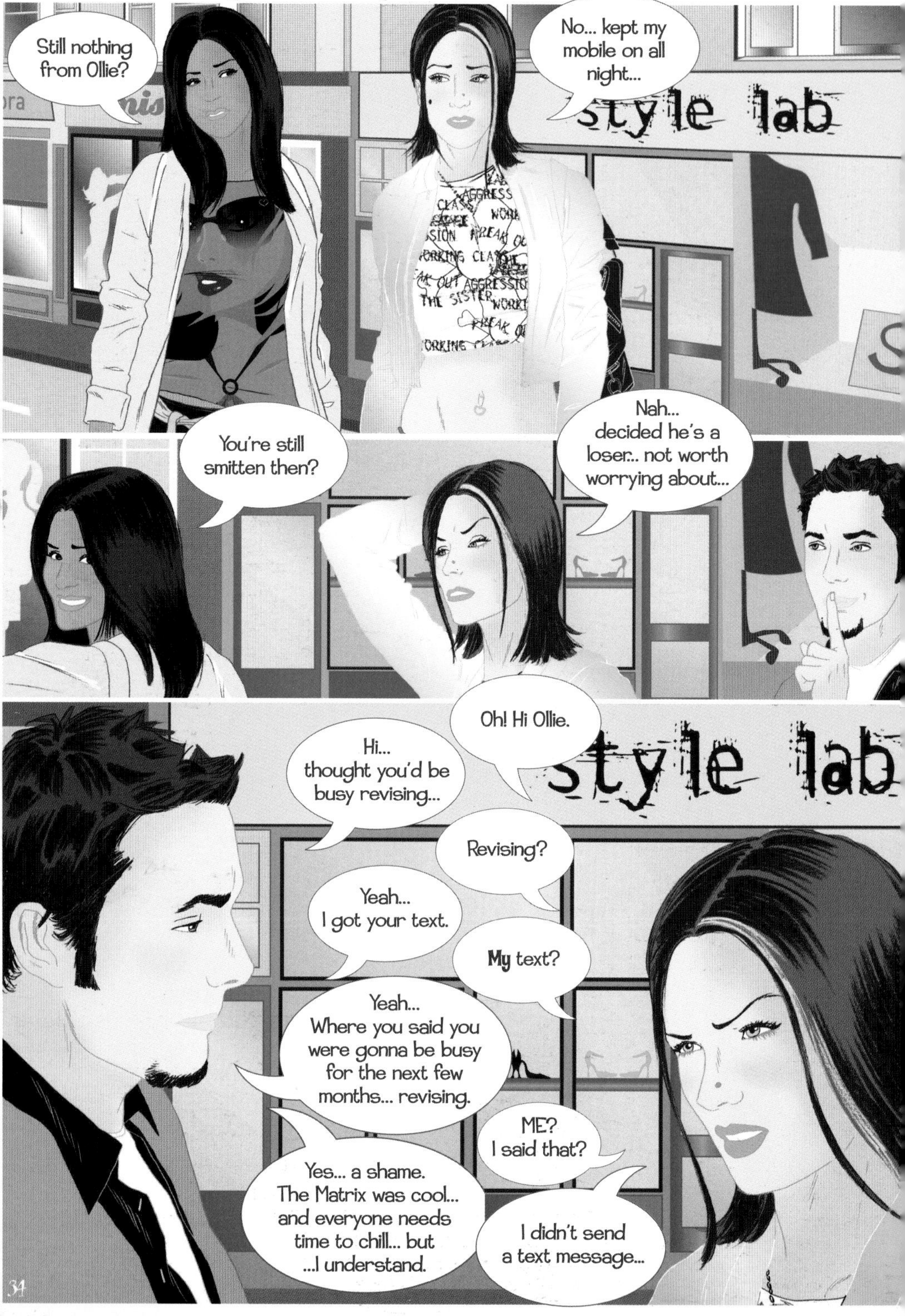

So who did, the fairies?

NO! The Ogre must have done that when she took my phone.

Now I'm really confused.

So, are you saying you'd like to go out again?

You bet!

Don't worry... you'll get used to her.

NUDGE NUDGE

I mean... Maybe...

Great... How about tomorrow night?

Oh no... I'm babysitting... Tell you what... I'll text you when the kid's gone to bed... you can come over.

Cool... I'll bring a DVD.

I can't believe the Ogre did that. She almost ruined my life. My whole destiny destroyed... my...

Come on Ella... you're heading for **MELODRAMA**. Don't get mad... get even.

What do you mean?

Time for the lovely Brian to send another message to Mabel I think...

i Melodrama

Short play in which the main roles are performed by women with large melons. Always very emotional stuff.

Ella is melodramatic - she's exaggerating her emotions. (In this case without the melons.)

37

Whale Attack!
Pop up primate
THE LIMIT
SPOUSE TRAP
CLUE DON'T
rabble

Let's have one game and one book and then I'll tuck you up in bed.

Mummy said you have to do all of them

Don't think so.

At last... there's a knock at the door...

46

49

Cool street chick

We're talking Attitude. Think Pink, Ms Dynamite, Ella.

Don't think Mrs Battye, Deirdre Barlow or Pauline Fowler... mnnn. Pauline bloody Fowler. Honestly. Anyone who says a cup of tea will cheer you up should look at the face on that. Like a bulldog chewing a wasp. I mean, we've seen some miserable people in our time but for God's sake. She must be the only woman who never has trouble getting her kids to school - they can't wait to get out of the flaming house! Or go to that fruit and veg stall. Or the pub.

Hell, they're probably throwing themselves under buses to keep out of that house and away from the moaning minging witch. Let's face it - Martin probably ran Jamie over so he could go to prison and get away from the hag. It's a wonder people don't throw themselves in the washing machines when she's in that launderette. Come on, how bad is it when you'd prefer to see Dot Cotton behind the desk there. The face that launched a thousand anti-depressants... and if you still don't believe us about Pauline Gargoyle Fowler, look how many of her on screen "family" have died or been written out. All of them. With the exception of Ian. And he's a dorkus maximus. Ladies and gentlemen of the jury, we rest our case.

Now you may be thinking that this is a long info panel but you need to know this and we're making up the rules as we go along, OK? And if any of you don't watch Eastenders ('Enders to the fans) you should know that what we just said was a) very funny and b) proof that we need to get out more... like Ella. Talking of which...

Actually, before we go, Pauline Fowler used to be in a sitcom with a woman called Mrs Slocombe. If you don't believe us, ask you parents about Mrs Slocombe's cat and see what they say. Dad will look amazed and Mum will probably just roll her eyes. Not that it's a powerful cat or anything but - oh here's a picture of Josh Hartnett to liven this up for you...

And here's Orlando Bloom...

Sorry, where were we? Oh. Yeah.
And our lack of social life. Well, Ella's really. Actually, speaking of Ella, better see how she's doing hadn't we?

❤JOSH❤   ❤ORLANDO❤

The door bell rings...

That will be Lettie... Have to go.

Can I come with you?

No.

But I hate walking to school on my own.

Then get some friends. Bye.

Mysti, I have some reservations... but Professor Dust has chosen you...

Mum, you're scaring me.

'Mum' is this another of your newfangled sayings? And fly, girl, don't use your legs.

What is this, Professor?

There's been a summoning, Mysti. We have to attend an **ASSEMBLY**...

i Assembly

1. A gathering of the whole school. They say it's to build a sense of community. We say it's an excuse for teachers to talk about things that interest them. Like canoeing. Or football results. Rare dogs. The smart girl will listen carefully and use this information later... (See "**Distracting teachers**".)

2. In the fairy world, Assembly is the gathering together of representatives of all the denizens of the hidden world. Each race sends two elders and two youngers.

The walk to school...

Baseball

1. American rounders for men who spit.
2. Analogy for relationship development:
   a. **FIRST BASE**- Serious snogging
   b. **SECOND BASE**- Chumba access
   c. **THIRD BASE**- CENSORED
   d. **HOME RUN**- After the wedding

NOTE: Watch out for boys who attempt the reverse order.

Hamsters

Cute, furry, loveable creatures. Their main claim to fame is that they can fit two packets of peanuts in their cheek pouches.

You've been chosen, Mysti.

Yes, but I don't want to make a fool of myself in front of Thorn...

You mean after the rapping?

No... the rapping was cool... I just sometimes get things wrong...

You won't. What's the Assembly about anyway?

It's the DROW ELVES. They summoned the gathering. No one knows why...

i Drow Elves

We warned you about them last time. Drow Elves are elves fallen from grace. Man sized, with silver skin and jet black or flame hair, they are secretive and **very** scary.

We'll be OK, Mysti, I promise.

Of course we will. The people of the hidden world have never fought each other in their lives.

Hmmm...

Who's in charge?

What are Assemblies like?

Boring mostly.
You have to put up with the Elves being snooty, the Leprechauns getting drunk and mischievous and the Gnomes talking about fishing. And that's for starters. But they can be fun. The Dragons come in animal form.

The Woodfather, Mysti. He's in charge.

The Woodfather?

Dragons?

Don't worry.
You just see a bright coloured animal: a robin red breast - Red Dragon, Gold Crested Chaffinch - Gold one.

i Dragons

Now we all know that Dragons wear Red, but there's a bit more to it. There are all sorts of Dragons. Red (mainly Chinese but in Wales too) Gold (discovered in America), Blue (Swedish and also North and South Pole), White (Russian) and Black (African).

63

This is what she'd call a 'vent'... This is wonderful...

But where are the Drows?

And if anyone should be bleating here it should be me - I was having a pint. And teleporting takes it out of ya to be sure, to be sure.

If my vulgar colleague has had his say, may I motion that, because of the Drow's flagrant disrespect -

Rivanor, you talk too much...

Enter Nero Vri'kaa leader of the Drow...

Apologies, brothers, sisters. Apologies, Woodfather. Wanted to make sure you were all here...

Wanted a dramatic entrance more like...

They need us. They're a younger species than all of us.

And the most violent, destructive enemy we have ever encountered. Even the Dragon Wars produced nothing like the carnage they inflict on themselves and anyone they can steal from. Woodfather, ask the Sylphs how many trees they lose. How they carve into them for pleasure!

Young Rainbowfrost is right, as is Master Oakwood, Nero. They are young, would you punish your child, Sk'alath, there, while he is still learning.

Woodfather, if his ignorance and evil nature threatened the balance of ours, I would cut his heart out before my brothers and sisters right now.

He's a monster. A...

Save your breath. I come here to launch an alliance – an alliance to save our world from the humans that threatened to destroy it. There is not one here, save the mighty dragons, who can claim they have not been affected by the plague. Humanity, I say, from today, we sever all relations with these killers –

You can't do that!

Meanwhile...

Ella's bedroom...

I'm gonna have to cut some more off to make it even... You could do with some colour too, brighten it up... I think Mum has some.

That's OK... I'm sick of having long hair anyway... my mum wouldn't let me cut it.

And your clothes... they're covered in mud... I wonder if there's anything you could borrow of mine.

It wouldn't fit me... I'm such a whale.

How about we go shopping... there's a sale on in Wow Thing...

I never dare go in there...

Well, tomorrow after school you're coming with me.

93

That's well funny...
Wait 'til I tell
everyone...

Laxative chocolate

Look in your granny's handbag; there's bound to be some. Because the most important thing in Grandma's life is a regular bowel movement.
Found it? **NO!** Don't eat it. OK. it looks like chocolate, smells like chocolate and, yes, more or less it tastes like chocolate. But it isn't. It will have you confined to the loo for the rest of the day. And let's face it, regular bowel movements are not top on your list of priorities, are they?

Mrs Battye takes over the dance floor...

That's the trouble
with men...
no one teaches
them to dance
properly...

It's OK, Brian... you
don't have to say
anything... it's
enough to know you
feel the same.

94

The guys come to help Rachael...
O-my-God...
She seems to have managed on her own!
Where're the bogs?
Wait for me, Jules...
Got the runs, girls? That was pretty amazing, Rach!
Yeah... I don't know what came over me.
I'm sorry Rick... I have to go now...
But you've been going all evening...
Strict parents... You know... I'll see you soon.
In a quiet corner...
Thanks Mysti... You look great... Good luck with Thorn...